NEW
REVISED
VALUES FOR
1983

PRICE GUIDE FOR

Madame Alexander

COLLECTOR'S DOLLS

D0101496

Published by:
COLLECTOR BOOKS
P.O. Box 3009
Paducah, Kentucky 42001

No.9

The current values in this book should be used only as a guide. They are not intended to set prices, which vary from one section of the country to another. Auction prices as well as dealer prices vary greatly and are affected by condition as well as demand. Neither the Author nor the Publisher assumes responsibility for any losses that might be incurred as a result of consulting this guide.

Additional copies of this book may be ordered from:

COLLECTOR BOOKS
P.O. Box 3009
Paducah, Kentucky 42001

@$3.95 Add $1.00 for postage and handling.

Copyright: Patricia R. Smith, 1983
ISBN: 0-89145-232-X

Printed by IMAGE GRAPHICS, Paducah, Kentucky

ABOUT PRICING

When the state of the economy becomes better adjusted the prices of Madame Alexander dolls may increase once more. We will just have to wait and see. Right now there is a lot of "wheeling and dealing" going on. The dealers have found that the doll buyer has all of a sudden become very discriminating. A doll collector used to go to a doll show, read the doll publications, and order any doll that sounded, or looked good to them. They are no longer acting in this fast manner, but have become extremely selective in their buying. This statement also holds true in all levels of collecting, be it dolls, stamps, fine arts, or whatever, but the basic fact is with us, as the old saying goes, "It's a buyers market."

We have seen the entire collecting/investing spectrum, from thousands of people getting into the collector field, to the stand off of not knowing exactly which way to turn, to the final oddity of collecting new dolls. Collectors wanted to collect something. When they found they could not afford older dolls or more affluent collectors found they had just about all they needed or wanted, each segment turned to the more reasonably priced new dolls on the store shelves. Now that aspect of our collecting field has become a jungle of madness!

If you cannot find CURRENT Madame Alexander dolls on the toy store shelves be prepared to pay the following prices on the 'secondary/investory' market: 8" - $35.00, $30.00 and $28.00; 8" Storybooks from $32.00 to $40.00; 1981 Pussy Cat - $60.00 to $68.00; 12" Laurie -$55.00; 12" Blue Boy, Romeo or the girls, Juliet or Pinky from $45.00 to $100.00; 14" Bride, Cinderella, Sleeping Beauty, Heidi, McGuffey Ana, Rebecca at $55.00 to $60.00; Elise Ballerina at $60.00 to $65.00. The set of CURRENT Little Women will run you just about $235.00. Gone with the Wind (Scarlet) $75.00. The large Victoria $40.00 and in Christening gown $58.00. Mark Anthony/Cleopatra, or Napoleon and Josephine will cost you from $100.00 to $135.00 per set. You can shake your head and say it isn't fair, but it is with us, and we can blame no one but ourselves for allowing it to happen!

Prices for this booklet are gathered from many places AND ARE ACTUAL PRICES PAID FOR MADAME ALEXANDER dolls. Prices are based on really clean, mint dolls. Any that are called 'tissue mint' . . . which means they are in the box, and have NEVER been played with or touched since they were made, will bring higher prices. Please remember two things: a Price GUIDE is that, a GUIDE and not the "last" word, and we are all individuals who have the last words in our own dealings . . . we do not have to buy unless we feel the doll is worth it, and that we can afford it . . . not just because it is a Madame Alexander doll. There are other dolls to be collected and enjoyed.

3

Madame Alexander dolls are still most desirable and most beautiful, and I hope many of you will be able to continue to build the collections you so desire.

The following are the "faces" of Alexander Dolls that have been used over and over. You will see a name after the dolls in this listing and this is the "face" of the doll (There may be a few exceptions.)

Wendy Ann (Compo.)

Tiny & Little Betty

Princess Elizabeth

Maggie

4

Margaret (O'Brien)

Cissy

Elise

Cissette

5

Lissy

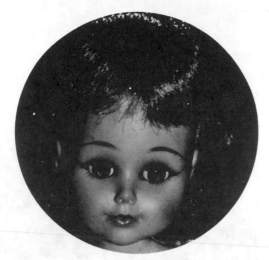

Coco

Jacqueline

6

Mary Ann

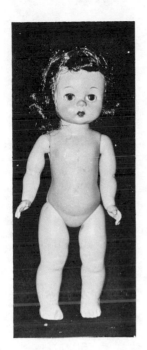

**1st Wendy Ann
Hard Plastic
1953 - 1954**

**Bend Knees
1956 - 1972**

**Powdery Straight Leg
(Non-Walker)
1973 to Date**

7

A

Active Miss. 18" hp. (Violet/Cissy) 1954 . . . .   275.00
Adams, Abigail. President's Ladies.
   1978. Discontinued 200.00
Adams, Louisa. President's Ladies.
   1978. Discontinued 200.00
African. 8" hp. Discontinued (1966-1971) . . . .   350.00 up
Agatha. 18" hp. (Cissy) Me and My Shadow
   Series. 1954 . . . .   525.00
     8" Wendy Ann. hp. Americana Group.
1953-1954 . . . .   425.00
     21" Portrait. 1967. (Jacqueline) 425.00
       1974. (Jacqueline) 350.00
       1975. (Jacqueline) 325.00
       1976. (Jacqueline) 300.00
     11" Portrette. 1968. (Cissette) 425.00
Agnes. Cloth/felt. 1930's 400.00
   Cloth. Oliver Twist. 18". 1934. . . . .   450.00
Alexander Rag Time Dolls. Cloth. 1938 . . . .   350.00
Alexander-kins (Wendy Ann) 7½"-8" hp.
   7½" Straight legs, non-walker. 1953-1954 . . .   145.00
   7½" Straight leg, walkers. 1954-1955 . . . .   135.00
   8" Bend knee, walker. 1956-1964 . . . .   125.00
   8" Bend knee, non-walkers. 1965-1972 . . . . . .   125.00
   8" Straight legs, non-walkers. Marked with
     full name "Alexander" across backs. 1976 to
     date . . . .   S.A.
   8" Straight legs, non walkers. Marked "Alex"
1973-1975 . . . .   50.00
   Exclusive in Sewing Basket. 1966-1969 . . . . .   700.00
   In case/wardrobe. 1953-1957 . . . .   550.00 up
   In dresser. 1953 . . . .   550.00 up
   Tagged or boxed outfits only, that are not
unusual 20.00
   Unusual outfits such as riding habit,
     nurse, ballgowns, etc.   35.00-   65.00
Alice. 18" hp. (Maggie). 1951 . . . .   250.00
Alice In Wonderland
   Cloth. 1930 & 1933. 16" 350.00
   7" Compo. (Tiny Betty) 125.00
   9" Compo. (Little Betty) 200.00
   11"-14" Compo. (Wendy Ann) 250.00

14½"-18". Compo. (Margaret)	250.00-	300.00
21". Compo. (Margaret)....................	350.00	
15"-18" Compo. (Wendy Ann)	350.00-	400.00
14½" hp. (Margaret) 1948	275.00	
14" hp. (Maggie) 1950	250.00	
17"-23" hp. (Maggie & Margaret) 1950	225.00-	350.00
15"-18"-23" hp. (Maggie-Margaret) 1951.....	225.00-	300.00
14" hp. With Trousseau. (Maggie)	550.00 up	
29" Cloth/vinyl. (Barbara Jane). 1952	275.00	
8" hp. (Wendy Ann). 1955-1956	300.00	
12" Lissy. 1963	850.00 up	
14" Plastic/vinyl. (Mary Ann) 1966	S.A.	
8" hp. Disney Crest Colors. (Disneyland-World). Discontinued. 1972-1976	275.00	
Amanda. 8" hp. 1961 Americana Group. (Wendy Ann)	425.00	
American Babies. Cloth. 16"-18"	125.00	
American Child. 7"-8" Compo. (Tiny Betty). 1938	125.00	
American Girl. 7"-8" Compo. (Tiny Betty). 1938 .	125.00	
9"-11" Compo. (Little Betty-Wendy Ann). 1937	165.00	
8" hp. (Wendy Ann) 1962-1964	425.00	
American Tots. Cloth dressed in child's fashions	150.00	
AWVS (American Women's Volunteer Service) 14" Compo. (Wendy Ann) 1942	185.00	
Amish Boy. 8" hp. (Wendy Ann) Discontinued. 1966-1969	350.00 up	
Amish Girl. 8" hp. (Wendy Ann) Discontinued. 1966-1969	350.00 up	
Amy (See Little Women).		
Anna Ballerina. 18" Compo. (Wendy Ann) (Pavlova). 1940	225.00	
Annabelle. 15" hp. (Maggie). 1952	250.00	
15" Trousseau/trunk. 1952	550.00 up	
18" hp.	300.00	
20"-23" hp.	325.00-	400.00
Annie Laurie. 14" Compo. (Wendy Ann). 1937 ...	250.00	
17" Compo. (Wendy Ann). 1937	295.00	
Antoinette. 21" Compo. 1946	450.00	
Apple Annie. 8" hp. (Wendy Ann). Americana Group. 1954	425.00	
Argentine Boy. 8" hp. (Wendy Ann). Discontinued. 1965-1966	400.00	
Argentine Girl. 8" hp. (Wendy Ann). Discontinued. 1965-1972 with bend knees	100.00	
Argentine Girl. 8" hp. Straight legs. Marks: Alex. 1973-1976	50.00	
Argentine Girl. 8" hp. Straight legs. 1976 to date	S.A.	
Arlene Dahl. 18" hp. (Maggie). 1950-1951	475.00	

Artie. 12" Plastic/vinyl. (Smarty). Sold through
FAO Schwarz. 1962 .... 250.00
Aunt Agatha. 8" hp. (Wendy Ann). 1957 .... 425.00
Aunt Betsy. Cloth/felt. 1930's 250.00
Aunt Pitty Pat. 14"-17" Compo. 1939 .... 175.00- 250.00
   8" hp. (Wendy Ann). 1957 .... 425.00
Austria Boy. 8" hp. (Wendy Ann). 1974 to date.
   Straight Legs. Marks: Alex. 1973 .... 50.00
   Formally Tyrolean Boy .... S.A.
Austria Girl. 8" hp. (Wendy Ann). 1974 to date.
   Straight Legs. Marks: Alex. 1973 .... 50.00
   Formally Tyrolean Girl .... S.A.

B

Babbie. Cloth. Long thin legs. Inspired by Katherine
   Hepburn. (Little Minister) 275.00
Babs. 20" hp. (Maggie). 1949 .... 250.00
Babs Skater. hp. (Margaret). 15" 225.00
   18" hp.................................... 300.00
   21" hp.................................... 375.00
Comp. (Margaret). 18" 325.00
Babsie Baby. Compo./Cloth. Moving tongue 100.00
Babsie Skater (roller). (Prin. Eliz.). 1941. 15" 175.00
Baby Angel. 8" hp. (Wendy Ann). 1955 .... 900.00 up
Baby Betty. 10"-12". Compo. 1935-1936 .... 125.00
Baby Brother and Sister. Cloth/vinyl. (Mary Mine).
   20". 1977   Discontinued................... 80.00
   14" .... S.A.
Baby Clown. 8" hp. (Wendy Ann). Painted face. 1955   900.00 up
Baby Ellen. 14" (Black Sweet Tears). 1965-1972 .   100.00
Baby Genuis. 11" All cloth. 1930's 125.00
   11"-12". Compo./cloth 125.00
   16". Compo./cloth...................... 150.00
   18"-21". hp. head. 1949-1950 .... 150.00
   8" hp./vinyl. 1956...................... 95.00
Baby Jane. 16". Compo. 1935 .... 500.00
Baby Lynn. 20". Cloth/vinyl. 1973-discontinued
1976 .... 85.00
Baby McGuffey. 22"-24". Compo. 1937 .... 200.00
   20" Cloth/vinyl. 1971.................... 75.00
   17" Cloth/vinyl. Discontinued 1977 .... 65.00
Baby Precious. Cloth/vinyl. 14" 1975 only 65.00
   20" Cloth/vinyl. 1974 discontinued 1976 ..... 55.00
Baby in Louis Viulton trunk/wardrobe. Any year   450.00 up
Bad Little Girl. 16". Cloth. 1964. Blue dress
   (Mate to Good Little Girl) 75.00

Ballerina: Also see individual dolls, sans: Leslie,
  Margaret, etc.

11″-13″ Betty	175.00
11″-14″. Compo. (Wendy Ann). 1936-1938	175.00
17″. Compo. (Wendy Ann). 1938	185.00
8″ hp. (Wendy Ann). 1953-1956	145.00
16½″ hp. Elise. 1957-1958-1962	225.00
Marybel head. 1963	275.00
14″. Melinda. 1963	225.00
10″-11″ hp. (Cissette). 1957-1959	275.00
17″ Plastic/vinyl. (Elise)	S.A.
Barbara Jane. 29″. Cloth/vinyl. 1952	275.00
Barbary Coast. 11″ hp. (Cissette). 1962-1963	950.00 up
Beau Art Dolls. 18″ hp. 1953	525.00 up
Beau Brummel. Cloth	300.00
Beauty Queen. hp. 1961. (Cissette)	225.00
Belle Brummel. Cloth	300.00
Belgium. 8″ hp. (Wendy Ann). 1972 only. Bend knees	100.00
8″ Straight legs marks: Alex. 1973-1975	50.00
8″ Straight legs. 1976 to date	S.A.
7″ Compo. (Tiny Betty). 1935-1938	125.00
Best Man. 8″ hp. (Wendy Ann). 1955	225.00
Beth. See Little Women.	
Betsy Ross. 8″ hp. (Wendy Ann). 1967-1972	
Bend knees	100.00
Straight legs. Marks: Alex. 1973-1975	50.00
Straight legs. 1976 to date	S.A.
1976 Bicent.	165.00
Betty. (Tiny). 7″ Compo. 1935-1937	150.00
13″-14″. Compo. 1935	165.00
16″-18″. Compo.	225.00
14½″-17½″ hp. (Maggie). Sears-1951	200.00
30″ Plastic/vinyl. 1960	300.00
Bible Character Dolls. 8″ hp. (Wendy Ann). 1954	1,200.00 up
Bill/Billy. 8″ hp. (Wendy Ann). Boys clothes and hair style.	
1953	175.00
Groom. 1953-1957	225.00
Binnie. hp. (Cissy). 14″ Ballerina. 1956	165.00
15″-18″ hp. 1954	165.00- 200.00
25″ hp. 1954	250.00
18″ Plastic/vinyl. 1964	145.00
Binnie Walker. hp. (Cissy). 15″-18″. 1954	165.00- 200.00
15″ Skater. hp. 1955	185.00
25″ hp. 1954	225.00
15″ in trunks/wardrobe	450.00
Birthday Party. 8″ hp. (Wendy Ann). 1955	145.00

Bitsey. 11"-12". Compo. 100.00
    Head hp. 11"-16". 1951 . . . . 100.00- 125.00
    19"-26" 125.00- 200.00
    Cloth/vinyl. 12". 1965 . . . . 100.00
Blue Boy. Cloth. 16" 300.00
    7" Compo. (Tiny Betty) 165.00
    8" hp. (Wendy Ann). 1956 . . . . 350.00
    12" Plastic/vinyl. 1972 to date . . . . S.A.
Blue Danube. 18" hp. (Margaret). 1953-1954 . . . . 525.00 up
    8" hp. (Wendy Ann). 1953 . . . . 300.00
Bobby. 8" hp. (Wendy Ann). 1957 . . . . 175.00
    8" hp. (Maggie Mixup). 1960 . . . . 200.00
Bobby Q. Cloth. 1940 . . . . 500.00
Boliva. 8" hp. (Wendy Ann). Discontinued.
1963-1966 . . . . 350.00
Bonnie (Baby). Vinyl. 1954-1955. 16"-19" 75.00- 95.00
    24"-30" 100.00- 150.00
Bonnie Toddler. Cloth/hp. head/vinyl limbs.
18". 1951 . . . . 100.00
Bo Peep, Little
    7" Compo. (Tiny Betty). 1937 . . . . 125.00
    9"-11" Compo. (Little Betty-Wendy Ann). 1938 165.00
    7½" hp. (Wendy Ann). 1955 . . . . 200.00
    8" hp. (Wendy Ann). 1962-1972. Bend knees . 100.00
    8" hp. (Wendy Ann). 1973-1975, straight legs.
      Marks: Alex 50.00
    8" hp. (Wendy Ann). Straight legs. 1976 to date S.A.
Brazil. 7" Compo. (Tiny Betty). 1937 . . . . 125.00
    9" Compo. (Little Betty). 1938 . . . . 165.00
    8" hp. (Wendy Ann). 1965-1972. Bend knees . 100.00
    8" hp. (Wendy Ann). Straight legs. 1973-1975.
      Marks: Alex 50.00
    8 hp. (Wendy Ann). Straight legs. 1976 to date. S.A.
Brenda Starr. 12" hp. 1964 . . . . 165.00
Bride 7" Compo. (Tiny Betty). 1935-1939 . . . . 125.00
    9"-11" Compo. (Little Betty). 1936-1941 . . . . . 165.00
13"-14"-15". Compo. (Wendy Ann) 200.00
    Compo Wendy Ann in trunk/trousseau . . . . . . 450.00 up
    17"-18". Compo. (Wendy Ann) 250.00
    21"-22". Compo. (Wendy Ann) 275.00
    21" Compo. Royal Wedding/Portrait. 1945-1947 400.00
    14"-17" hp. (Margaret) (Maggie) 225.00
    17" hp. (Margaret) in pink. 1950 . . . . 265.00
    18" hp. (Margaret) Tagged: Prin. Eliz 350.00
    21" hp. (Margaret) (Maggie) 325.00
    16½" hp. (Elise). 1957, 1958 & 1964 . . . . 200.00
    16½" hp. (Elise). 1962 . . . . 225.00
    20" hp. (Cissy). 1956 . . . . 250.00
    25" hp. (Cissy). 1956 . . . . 300.00

10" hp. (Cissette). 1957 .... 150.00
10" hp. (Cissette) in trunk/trousseau .... 450.00 up
12" hp. (Lissy) 200.00
21" (Jacqueline) - 1965 .... 650.00
    1969 .... 395.00
8" hp. (Wendy Ann). 1953-1955 .... 200.00
1956-1958 .... 150.00
1960 .... 150.00
1963-1965 .... 125.00
1966-1972. Bend knees 100.00
1973-1975. Straight legs. Marks: Alex. 50.00
1976-to date. Straight legs .... S.A.
14" Plastic/vinyl. 1973-1976 .... 165.00
17" Plastic/vinyl. (Elise) .... S.A.
17" Plastic/vinyl. (Leslie) 200.00
17" Plastic/vinyl. (Polly) 200.00
Bridesmaid
    9" Compo. (Little Betty). 1937-1939 .... 150.00
    11"-14". Compo. (Wendy Ann) 200.00
    15"-18". Compo. (Wendy Ann) 225.00- 265.00
    20"-22". Compo. (Wendy Ann) Portrait 275.00
    21½" Compo. (Prin. Eliz) 275.00
    14"-17" hp. (Margaret-Maggie) 1850 .... 265.00
    19" Rigid vinyl. (Margaret) In pink, 1952-1953 300.00
    20" hp. (Cissy). 1955 .... 250.00
    10" hp. (Cissette). 1957 .... 165.00
    12" hp. (Lissy) 225.00
    16½" hp. (Elise). 1957 .... 200.00
    8" hp. (Wendy Ann). 1955 .... 175.00
        1956 .... 175.00
        1957-1958 .... 175.00
Brigitta. 11" & 14". See Sound of Music.
Buck Rabbit. Cloth/felt. 1930's 300.00
Bud. 16"-19". Cloth/vinyl. 1952 .... 100.00- 125.00
    25". 1953 .... 145.00
Bunny. 18" Plastic/vinyl. (Melinda). 1962 .... 225.00
Burma. 7" Compo. (Tiny Betty). 1939 .... 125.00
Butch. 11"-12" Compo/cloth 85.00
    14"-16" Compo/cloth 100.00
    14" Cloth/vinyl head/limbs. 1950 .... 75.00
    12" Cloth/vinyl. 1965 .... 75.00
Butch McGuffey. Compo/cloth. 1940 .... 125.00

C

Canada. 8" hp. (Wendy Ann). 1968-1972. Bend knees 100.00
    1973-1975. Straight legs. Marks: Alex 50.00
    1976 to date. Straight legs .... S.A.

13

Camille. 21" Compo. (Wendy Ann). 1938 . . . .   500.00
Carmen. (Note. Dressed like Carmen Miranda, but
  not marked or meant as such)
    7" Compo. (Tiny Betty). 1936-1938 . . . .   165.00
    9"-11" Compo. (Little Betty) Boy & Girl. 1937-
      1941 (Also see Rumbero/Rumbera) 200.00
    11"-13". Compo. (Wendy Ann) 200.00- 225.00
    15"-18". Compo. (Wendy Ann) 250.00- 300.00
    21" Compo. (Wendy Ann) 400.00
Carmen Portrait. 7"-8" Compo. (Tiny Betty) 165.00
    16"-18". Compo. (Wendy Ann) 300.00- 350.00
    21" Compo. (Wendy Ann). 1937-1939 . . . .   500.00
    14"-17" hp. (Margaret) 250.00- 350.00
Caroline. 15". Vinyl. 1961. In dresses 300.00
    In riding habit 375.00
    As boy/boy hair style (nude) 95.00
    In case/wardrobe . . . .   450.00 up
Carreen. 14"-17" (Wendy Ann). Compo. 1937 . . . .   175.00- 250.00
Carrot Top. 21" Cloth. 1967 . . . .   100.00
Cathy. 17"-21" Compo. (Wendy Ann). 1939 . . . . .   350.00
Century of Fashions (1854-1954). 14" & 18" hp.
  (Margaret, Maggie & Cissy) 350.00- 525.00
Charity. 8" hp. (Wendy Ann). Americana Group.
  1961 . . . .   425.00
Chatterbox. 24". Plastic/vinyl. 1961 . . . .   225.00
Cheri. 18" hp. (Margaret). 1954 . . . .   525.00
Cherry Twins. 8" hp. (Wendy Ann). 1957 . . . .   250.00 up
Cherub. 12". Vinyl. 1960 . . . .   95.00
    18" hp. head/cloth & vinyl 85.00
    26" 125.00
Cherub Babies. Cloth 250.00
China. 7" Compo. (Tiny Betty). 1936 . . . .   125.00
    8" hp. (Wendy Ann). 1972. Bend knees 100.00
    8" with Maggie Mixup head 165.00
    Straight legs. 1973-1975. Marks: Alex 50.00
    Straight legs. 1976 to date . . . .   S.A.
Christening Baby. 11"-13" Cloth/vinyl. 1951-1954   75.00
    16"-19" 85.00-   95.00
Cinderella. 7"-8" Compo. (Tiny Betty). 1935 . . . . .   165.00
    13" Compo. (Wendy Ann) 200.00
    15" Compo. (Betty). 1935-1937 . . . .   225.00
    14" Compo. (Prin. Eliz.) Sear's Exclusive. 1939   275.00
    16"-18" Compo. (Prin. Eliz.) 300.00
    14" hp. (Margaret). 1950. Ballgown 385.00
    14" hp. (Margaret). "Poor" outfit. 1950 . . . . .   385.00
    18" hp. (Margaret) 450.00
    12" hp. (Lissy Classic). 1966 . . . . 1,000.00 up
    8" hp. (Wendy Ann). 1955 . . . .   300.00

14

14" Plastic/vinyl. (Mary Ann). 1967 to date.
(Poor) .... S.A.
14" Plastic/vinyl. (Mary Ann). 1970 to date.
(Ballgown) .... S.A.
Cissette. 10"-11" hp. in various street dresses.
1957-1963 .... 145.00
In Ballgowns 250.00- 300.00
Special gift set/three wigs .... 450.00 up
Doll only 155.00
Queen/trunk/trousseau. 1954 .... 500.00 up
Cissy. 20" hp. (Also 21"). 1955-1959.
In various street dresses 175.00
In ballgowns 250.00- 500.00
Trunk/wardrobe .... 700.00 up
Magazine ad's using doll. 1950's 15.00
Civil War. 18" hp. (Margaret). 1953 .... 525.00
8" hp. (Wendy Ann). 1953-1954 .... 425.00
Clarabell Clown. 19". 1951 .... 165.00
29" 225.00
49" 350.00
Clover Kid. 7" Compo 165.00
Coco. 21" Plastic/vinyl. 1966. In various clothes
other than Portrait .... 1,700.00 up
Colonial. 7" Compo. (Tiny Betty). 1937-1938 .... 165.00
9" Compo. (Little Betty). 1936-1939 .... 200.00
8" hp. (Wendy Ann) 1962-1964 .... 350.00
Cookie. 19" Compo/cloth. 1938 .... 125.00
Cornelia. 21" Portrait Series. 1972 .... 425.00
1973 .... 425.00
1974 .... 400.00
1975 .... 350.00
1976 .... 300.00
1978 .... 225.00
Cloth/felt. 1930's 300.00
Country Cousins. 10" Cloth 75.00
26" Cloth 175.00
30" Cloth 200.00
16½" (Marybel) 1958 .... 165.00
Cousin Grace. 8" hp. (Wendy Ann). 1956 .... 425.00
Cousin Karen. 8" hp. (Wendy Ann). 1956 .... 425.00
Cousin Marie & Mary. 8" hp. (Wendy Ann) 425.00
Cowboy. 8" hp. (Wendy Ann) Discontinued
1967-1969 .... 400.00
Cowgirl. 8" hp. (Wendy Ann) Discontinued
1967-1979 .... 400.00
Cry Dollie. 14"-16" Vinyl. 1963 .... 85.00
20" 100.00

Cuddly. 10½" Cloth. 1942	100.00
17" Cloth. 1942	125.00
Curly Locks. 7½" hp. (Wendy Ann). 1955	250.00
Cynthia. 15" hp. (Black Margaret). 1952	495.00
18"	550.00
23"	650.00
Czechoslovakia. 8" hp. (Wendy Ann).	
1972. Bend knees	100.00
1973-1975. Straight legs. Marks: Alex	50.00
1976 to date. Straight legs	S.A.
7" Compo. (Tiny Betty). 1935-1937	125.00

D

Danish. 7" Compo. (Tiny Betty). 1937	125.00
9" Compo. (Little Betty). 1938	165.00
David Copperfield. 7" Compo. (Tiny Betty)	200.00
14" Compo. (Wendy Ann). 1938	350.00
16" Cloth Dicken's Character	400.00
David Quack-a-field or Twistail. Cloth/felt. 1930's	300.00
Davy Crockett Boy. 8" hp. (Wendy Ann). 1955	350.00
Davy Crockett Girl. 8" hp. (Wendy Ann). 1955	400.00
Day of Week Dolls. 7" (Tiny Betty)	165.00
9"-11" Compo. (Little Betty). 1936-1938	200.00
13" Compo. (Wendy Ann)	265.00
Dearest. 12" Baby	95.00
Debutant. 18" hp. (Maggie). 1953	525.00
Degas. 21" Compo. Portrait. 1945	500.00
Degas Girl. 14" Plastic/vinyl. (Mary Ann)	
1967 to date	S.A.
Denmark. 11" hp. (Cissette). 1962	950.00 up
8" hp. (Wendy Ann). 1970-1972. Bend knees	100.00
8" hp. (Wendy Ann). Straight legs. Marks: Alex.	
1973-1975	50.00
8" hp. (Wendy Ann). Straight legs. 1976 to date	S.A.
Dicksie & Ducksie. Cloth/felt. 1930's	300.00
Dilly Dally Sally. 7"-8" Compo (Tiny Betty). 1937	165.00
9" Compo. (Little Betty). 1938	200.00
Ding Dong Dell. 7" Compo. (Tiny Betty). 1937	165.00
Dionne Quints. 20" Compo. Toddlers	450.00 each
	2,400.00 set
19" Compo. Toddlers	400.00 each
	2,200.00 set
16"-17" Compo. Toddlers	375.00 each
	2,000.00 set
14" Compo. Toddlers	300.00 each
	1,800.00 set

11" Compo. Toddlers. Wigs & sleep eyes	225.00 each	
	1,600.00 set	
11" Compo. Toddlers. Molded hair & sleep eyes	225.00 each	
	1,600.00 set	
11" Compo. Babies. Wigs & sleep eyes......	225.00 each	
	1,600.00 set	
11" Compo. Babies. Molded hair & sleep eyes	225.00 each	
	1,600.00 set	
8" Compo. Toddlers. Mold hair & painted eyes	135.00 each	
	900.00 set	
8" Compo. Toddlers. Wigs and painted eyes .	135.00 each	
	900.00 set	
7½"-8" Babies. Molded hair and painted eyes	135.00 each	
	900.00 set	
14" Cloth body/compo....................	425.00 each	
	2,000.00 set	
17" Cloth body/compo....................	475.00 each	
	2,200.00 set	
24" All cloth	650.00	
16" All cloth............................	525.00	
Dolls of the Month. 7"-8" Compo. (Tiny Betty). 1936	165.00	
Dolly Dryper. 11" Vinyl. 1952	95.00	
Doris Keane. Cloth.........................	300.00	
9"-11" Compo. (Little Betty). 1936	175.00-	195.00
Dottie Dumbunnie. Cloth/felt. 1930's..........	300.00	
Dr. Dafoe. 14" Compo. 1937	450.00	
15"-16" Compo.	500.00	
Dressed For Opera. 18" hp. (Margaret)	525.00	
Drum Majorette. 7½" hp. (Wendy Ann). 1955 ...	425.00	
Dude Ranch. 8" hp. (Wendy Ann). 1955	185.00	
Dumplin' Baby. 23½". 1957	85.00	
Dutch. 7" Compo. (Tiny Betty). 1935-1939	125.00	
*8" Boy hp. (Wendy Ann). 1964-1972. Bend knees	100.00	
8" hp. Straight legs. Marks: Alex. 1972-1975	50.00	
8" hp. Straight legs. 1976 to date	S.A.	
*8" hp. Girl. (Wendy Ann). 1961-1972. Bend knees	100.00	
8" hp. Straight legs. 1973-1975. Marks: Alex	50.00	
8" hp. Straight legs. 1976 to date	S.A.	
8" Maggie Mixup face....................	165.00	
*Both became "Netherland" in 1974		

E

Easter Doll. 8" hp. (Wendy Ann). 1968	975.00 up	
14" Plastic/vinyl. (Mary Ann). 1968	1,200.00 up	
Ecuador. 8" hp. (Wendy Ann). Discontinued.		
1963-1966	350.00 up	

Edith, The Lonely Doll. 16" Plastic/vinyl. 1958 . . 200.00
   22" 265.00
   8" hp. (Wendy Ann) 350.00
Edith With Golden Hair. Cloth. 18" 300.00
Edwardian. 18" hp. (Margaret). 1953 . . . . 525.00 up
Egyptian. 7"-8"Compo. (Tiny Betty). 1936 . . . . . . 165.00
   9" Compo. (Little Betty). 1936 . . . . 200.00
Elaine. 18" hp. (Cissy). 1954 . . . . 525.00
   8" hp. (Wendy Ann). 1954 . . . . 425.00
Elise. 16½" hp./vinyl arms. 1957-1960
   In street clothes . . . . 185.00 up
   In ballgowns . . . . 200.00 up
   With Marybel head. 1962 . . . . 185.00 up
   With Bouffant Hairstyle. 1963 only . . . . 185.00 up
   17" 1961-1962. hp./vinyl arms 145.00
   18" 1963-1964 . . . . 125.00
   In riding habit 195.00
   17" 1967-1970 . . . . 125.00
   17" in trunk/troussea. 1966, 67, 68, 69, 70,
     71, 72 . . . . 450.00 up
   17" Portait. Discontinued 1974 . . . . 250.00
17" In Formal. Discontinued 1977 . . . . 250.00
Elizabeth Monroe 200.00
Emily. Cloth/felt. 1930's 300.00
English Guard. 8" hp. (Wendy Ann)
Discontinued. 1966-1968 . . . . 475.00
Eskimo. 8" hp. (Wendy Ann). Discontinued.
   1967-1969 . . . . 475.00
   With Maggie Mixup face 525.00
Evangeline. 18" Cloth 300.00
Eva Lovelace. 7" Compo. (Tiny Betty). 1935 . . . . 165.00
   Cloth 300.00

F

Fairy Princess. 7"-8" Compo. (Tiny Betty). 1940 . 165.00
   9" Compo. (Little Betty). 1939-1940 . . . . 200.00
   11" Compo. (Wendy Ann) 200.00
   15"-18" Compo. (Wendy Ann) 225.00- 275.00
   21"-22" Compo. (Wendy Ann) 300.00- 325.00
Fairy Queen. 14½" Compo. (Wendy Ann). 1940 . . 225.00
   18" Compo. (Wendy Ann) 275.00
   18" hp. (Margaret) 350.00
   14½" hp. (Margaret). 1948 . . . . 265.00
Fairy Tales-Dumas. 9" Compo. (Little Betty). 1940 200.00
Faith 8" hp. (Wendy Ann). Americana Group. 1961 425.00
Finland. 8" hp. (Wendy Ann). Bend knees. 1968-1972 100.00
   8" hp. Straight legs. 1973-1975. Marks: Alex 50.00

18

8" hp. Straight legs. 1976 to date . . . . S.A.
Finnish. 7" Compo. (Tiny Betty). 1935-1937 . . . . . 125.00
First Communion. 8" hp. (Wendy Ann). 1957 . . . . 275.00
Fisher Quints. 7" hp./vinyl. (Little Genuis). 1964. 325.00 set
Five Little Peppers. Compo. 13" & 16". 1936 . . . . 250.00- 350.00
Flora McFlimsey. (with and without "e")
   22" Compo. (Prin. Eliz.) 450.00
   15"-16" Compo. (Prin. Eliz.) 375.00
   16"-17" Compo. (Wendy Ann) 375.00
   14" Compo. (Prin. Eliz.) 350.00
   12" Compo. Holds 5" Nancy Ann Doll
     Tagged Margie Ann (Wendy Ann) 300.00
   15" Miss. (Cissy). 1953 . . . . 375.00
Flowergirl. 16"-18" Compo. (Prin. Eliz.) 225.00- 265.00
   20"-24" Compo. (Prin. Eliz.) 275.00
   15"-18" hp. (Cissy). 1954 . . . . 185.00- 250.00
   15" hp. (Margaret). 1954 . . . . 265.00
   8" hp. (Wendy Ann). 1956 . . . . 200.00
France. 7" Compo. (Tiny Betty). 1936 . . . . 125.00
Frederich: See Sound of Music.
French. 8" hp. (Wendy Ann). Bend knees. 1961-1972 100.00
   8" hp. Straight legs. 1973-1975. Mark: Alex . 50.00
   8" Straight legs. 1976 to date . . . . S.A.
French Flowergirl. 8" hp. (Wendy Ann). 1956 . . . 300.00
Frou-Frou. 40" Cloth in green Ballerina dress. 1951 375.00
Funny. 18" Cloth. 1963. Discontinued 65.00

G

Gainsbourgh. 20" hp. (Cissy). 1957 . . . . 400.00
   10" hp. (Cissette). 1968-1969 . . . . 300.00
     1970 . . . . 300.00
   21" hp./vinyl arms. (Jacqueline). 1968 . . . . 425.00
   21" (Jacqueline). 1972 . . . . 425.00
   21" (Jacqueline). 1973 . . . . 425.00
   21" (Jacqueline). 1978 . . . . 275.00
Garden Party. 18" hp. (Margaret). 1953 . . . . 525.00
   20" hp. (Cissy). 1956-1957 . . . . 400.00
Gardening. 8" hp. (Wendy Ann). 1955 . . . . 165.00
Gene Tierney. 1945. Compo. (Wendy Ann) 14"-17" 275.00- 325.00
Genius Baby. 21"-30". Plastic/vinyl 50.00- 95.00
German. 8" hp. (Wendy Ann). Bend knees.
1966-1972 . . . . 100.00
   8" hp. Straight legs. 1973-1975. Marks: Alex 50.00
   8" Straight legs. 1976 to date . . . . S.A.
Gibson Girl. 10" hp. (Cissette). 1962 . . . . 950.00 up
   1963 (Plain non-striped blouse) . . . . 950.00 up
   16" Cloth. 1930's 300.00
Gidget. 14" Plastic/vinyl. (Mary Ann). 1966 . . . . . 250.00

19

Ginger Rogers. Compo. (Wendy Ann)
14"-21". 1940-1945 . . . . 300.00- 450.00
Girl On Flying Trapeze. 40" Cloth. Pink satin tu-tu
1951 . . . . 375.00
Glamour Girls of 1953. hp. 18" (Margaret-Maggie) 525.00
Godey. 21" Compo. 1945. (Wendy Ann) 500.00
    14" hp. (Margaret). 1950 . . . . 400.00
    20" hp. (Margaret). 1951 . . . . 465.00
    18" hp. (Maggie). 1953 . . . . 525.00
    21" hp./vinyl straight arms. (Cissy). 1961 . . . 400.00
    21" (Jacqueline). 1965 . . . . 500.00
    21" hp./vinyl arms (Jacqueline). 1967 . . . . 425.00
      1969 . . . . 400.00
      1970 . . . . 350.00
      1971 . . . . 325.00
    11" hp. (Cissette). 1968 . . . . 425.00 up
      1969 . . . . 425.00 up
      1970 . . . . 425.00 up
    21" Plastic/vinyl (Coco). 1966 . . . . 1,500.00 up
Godey Lady. 14" hp. (Margaret) 400.00
    18" hp. (Margaret) 465.00
Godey Bride. 14" hp. (Margaret) 400.00
    18" hp. (Margaret) 525.00
Godey Groom/Man. hp. (Margaret). 14" 475.00
    18" hp. (Margaret) 525.00
Goes Visiting. 8" hp. (Wendy Ann). 1955 . . . . 165.00
Going to See Grandma. 8" hp. (Wendy Ann). 1955 145.00
Gold Rush. 11" hp. (Cissette). 1963 . . . . 950.00 up
Goldilocks. 18" Cloth. 1930's 300.00
    7"-8" Compo. (Tiny Betty). 1938 . . . . 165.00
    18" hp. (Maggie). 1951 . . . . 525.00
    14" Plastic/vinyl. (Mary Ann). 1978 . . . . S.A.
Good Fairy. hp. 14" (Margaret) 285.00
Good Little Girl. 16" Cloth. Pink Dress.
(Mate to Bad Little Girl) 100.00
Goya. 8" hp. (Wendy Ann). 1953 . . . . 450.00
    21" hp./vinyl arms. (Jacqueline). 1968 . . . . 500.00
Graduation. 8" hp. (Wendy Ann). 1957 . . . . 275.00
    12" (Lissy) 450.00
Grandma Jane. 14" Plastic/vinyl (Mary Ann). 1970 200.00
Grave Alice. Cloth. 18" 300.00
Great Britian. 8" hp. (Wendy Ann). 1977 to date S.A.
Greek Boy. 8" hp. (Wendy Ann)
Discontinued. 1965-1968 . . . . 350.00 up
Greek Girl. 8" hp. (Wendy Ann). Bend knees.
1968-1972 . . . . 100.00
    8" hp. Straight legs. 1973-1975. Marks: Alex 50.00
    8" hp. Straight legs. 1976 to date . . . . S.A.

Gretel. 7" Compo. (Tiny Betty). 1937 .... 165.00
   9" Compo. (Little Betty). 1938 .... 200.00
   7½"-8" hp. (Wendy Ann). 1955 .... 200.00
   8" hp. (Wendy Ann). 1966-1972. Bend knees . 100.00
   8" hp. Straight legs. 1973-1975. Marks: Alex   50.00
   8" hp. Straight legs. 1976 to date .... S.A.
Gretl. See Sound of Music.
Groom. 18"-21" Compo. 375.00
   18"-21" hp 375.00
   14"-16" hp. (Margaret) 300.00
   7½" hp. (Wendy Ann). 1953-1955 .... 225.00
   8" hp. (Wendy Ann). 1961-1963 .... 175.00
Guardian Angel. 8" hp. (Wendy Ann). 1954 ..... 900.00 up
   8" hp. (Maggie Mixup) 1,000.00

H

Hansel. 7" Compo. (Tiny Betty). 1937 .... 165.00
   9" Compo. (Little Betty). 1938 .... 200.00
   7½" hp. (Wendy Ann). 1955 .... 250.00
   8" hp. (Wendy Ann). Bend knees. 1966-1972 . 100.00
   8" hp. Straight legs. 1973-1975. Marks: Alex.   50.00
   8" hp. Straight legs. 1976 to date .... S.A.
Happy. 20" Cloth/vinyl. 1970 .... 200.00
Hawaiian. 8" hp. (Wendy Ann)
   Discontinued. 1966-1969 .... 350.00 up
   7" Compo. (Tiny Betty). 1936 .... 150.00
Hedy LaMarr. 17" hp. (Margaret). 1949 .... 425.00
Heidi. 7" Compo. (Tiny Betty) 165.00
   14" Plastic/vinyl. (Mary Ann). 1969 to date .. S.A.
Hello Baby. 22" 85.00
Helping Mama. 8" hp. (Wendy Ann). 1955 ...... 145.00
Hiawatha. 8" hp. (Wendy Ann)
   Discontinued. 1967-1969 .... 350.00 up
   7" Compo. (Tiny Betty) 165.00
   Cloth. 18" 325.00
Highland Fling. 8" hp. (Wendy Ann). 1955 ...... 165.00
Hilda. 18" Compo. (Margaret). Black doll. 1947 .. 500.00
Honeybea. 12" Vinyl. 1963 .... 95.00
Honeyette Baby. Compo/cloth. 1940 .... 65.00
Honeybun. 19"-23"-26". 1951 .... 65.00-   95.00
Hulda. 18" Compo. (Margaret). 1946 .... 425.00
Huggums, Little. 12" Molded hair. 1963 to date . S.A.
   12" Rooted hair. 1963 to date .... S.A.
Huggums, Big. 25". 1963 to date .... S.A.
   Brother and Sister. 25" .... S.A.
Hungarian. 8" hp. (Wendy Ann). Bend knees.
   1962-1972 .... 100.00

8" hp. Straight legs. 1973-1976. Marks: Alex   50.00
8" hp. Straight legs. 1976 to date . . . .   S.A.

I

Ice Capades. (Cissy) . . . .   450.00 up
Ice Capades. (Jacqueline) . . . .   1,000.00 up
Ice Skater. 8" hp. (Wendy Ann). 1954-1956 . . . . .   165.00
India. 8" hp. (Wendy Ann). Bend knees. 1965-1972   100.00
    8" hp. Straight legs. 1973-1975. Marks: Alex   50.00
    8" hp. Straight legs. 1976 to date . . . .   S.A.
Indian Boy. 8" hp. (Wendy Ann). Discontinued. 1966   425.00
Indian Girl. 8" hp. (Wendy Ann). Discontinued. 1966   425.00
Indonesia. 8" hp. (Wendy Ann). 1970-1972
    Bend knees 100.00
    8" hp. Straight legs. 1972-1975. Marks: Alex   50.00
    8" hp. Straight legs. 1976 to date . . . .   S.A.
    With Maggie Mixup face 200.00
Irish. 8" hp. (Wendy Ann). Bend knees. 1964-1972   100.00
    8" hp. Straight legs. 1973-1975. Marks: Alex   50.00
    8" hp. Straight legs. 1976 to date. . . . .   S.A.
Irish. 10" (Cissette). 1963 . . . .   950.00 up
Israeli. 8" hp. (Wendy Ann). 1965-1972. Bend knees   100.00
    8" hp. Straight legs. 1973-1975. Marks: Alex   50.00
    8" hp. Straight legs. 1976 to date . . . .   S.A.
Italy. 8" hp. (Wendy Ann). 1961-1972. Bend knees   100.00
    8" hp. Straight legs. 1973-1975. Marks: Alex.   50.00
    8" hp. Straight legs. 1976 to date . . . .   S.A.

J

Jack & Jill. 7"-8" Compo. (Tiny Betty). 1938-1939   165.00
    9" Compo. (Little Betty). 1939 only 200.00
Jacqueline in Riding Habit . . . .   700.00 up
    In gown from cover of 1962 catalog 600.00
Jacqueline. 21" hp./vinyl arms. 1961-1962. . . . . . .   700.00
    10" hp. (Cissette). 1962 . . . .   475.00
Jacqueline. Exclusive in trunks with wardrobes:
1962 . . . .   950.00 up
    1966 . . . .   950.00 up
    1967 . . . .   750.00 up
Jane Withers. 1937. Compo.
    12"-13½" (Closed mouth) 675.00
    15"-17" 675.00
    17" with cloth body 700.00
    18"-19" 725.00
    19"-20" (Closed mouth) 850.00
    20"-21" 850.00
Janie. 36". Plastic/vinyl. 1960 . . . .   225.00
    12" Toddler. 1964 . . . .   200.00

22

14" Baby. 1972	95.00
20" Baby. 1972	125.00
Japan. 8" hp. (Wendy Ann). 1968-1972. Bend knees	100.00
8" hp. Straight legs. 1973-1975. Marks: Alex.	50.00
8" hp. Straight legs. 1976 to date	S.A.
With Maggie Mixup face	250.00
Jeannie Walker. 13"-14" Compo.	275.00
18" Compo.	400.00
Jenny Lind. 21" hp./vinyl arms. (Jacqueline). 1969	600.00
1970	600.00
11" hp. (Cissette). 1969	500.00
1970 (With lace trim)	500.00
14" Plastic/vinyl. (Mary Ann). 1970	450.00
Jenny Lind & Listening Cat	
14" Plastic/vinyl. (Mary Ann). 1969	425.00
Jo. See Little Women.	
Joanie. 36" Plastic/vinyl. 1960	225.00
36" Nurse. 1960	250.00
John Power's Models. hp. (Maggie & Margaret). 1952	
14"	525.00
18"	600.00
Judy. 21" Compo. (Wendy Ann). 1945	500.00
21" hp./vinyl arms. (Jacqueline). 1962	500.00
Jogo-slav. 7" Compo. (Tiny Betty). 1935-1937	125.00
Juliet. 21" Compo. (Wendy Ann)	500.00
18" Compo. (Wendy Ann). 1937	400.00
8" hp. (Wendy Ann). 1955	750.00 up
12" Plastic/vinyl. (Nancy Drew).1978	S.A.
June Bride. 21" Compo.	500.00
June Wedding. 8" hp. (Wendy Ann). 1956	165.00

K

Karen. 15"-18" hp. 1948-1949. (Margaret)	250.00	
Karen Ballerina. 15" Compo. (Margaret). 1947	250.00	
18"-21"	400.00	
Kate Greenaway. Cloth. 16"	400.00	
13"-14"-15" Compo. (Prin. Eliz.)	300.00-	350.00
18"	400.00	
24"	500.00	
Kathleen. 23" Vinyl (Rigid). 1959	165.00	
Kathryn Grayson. 20"-21" hp. (Margaret). 1949	425.00	
Katie. 12" Plastic/vinyl. (Black Smarty). 1963	225.00	
12" hp. (Lissy). 1962 Anniversary doll for FAO Schwarz	1,000.00 up	
Kathy. 15"-18" hp. (Maggie). 1951	285.00	
11"-13" Vinyl. 1955-1956	85.00	

Kathy Baby. 13"-15" Vinyl. Rooted hair. 1954 .. 75.00
 18"-21" 85.00
 11" Vinyl. Molded hair 65.00
 15"-19". 1955 .... 75.00
 21"-25" 95.00
Kathy Cry Dolly. 11"-15". Vinyl. 1957 .... 75.00
 18"-21" 85.00
Kathy Tears. 11"-15"-17". Vinyl. 1957 .... 70.00
 19"-23"-26" 80.00- 95.00
 12"-16"-19" Vinyl (New face). 1960-1961 ..... 65.00- 75.00
Kelly. 12" hp. (Lissy). 1959 .... 300.00
 15"-16" (Marybel). 1958 .... 200.00
 16" in trunk/wardrobe. 1959 .... 450.00 up
 22" 350.00
King. Compo. 21". 1942-1946 .... 425.00
Kitten. 14"-18" Cloth/vinyl. 1962 .... 65.00
 24". 1961 .... 70.00
 20". 1968 .... 50.00
Kitten Kries. 20" Cloth/vinyl. 1967 .... 65.00
Kitty Baby. 21" Compo. 1941 .... 85.00
Klondike Kate. 11" hp. (Cissette). 1963 .... 950.00 up
Korea. 8" hp. (Wendy Ann)
 Discontinued. 1968-1970 .... 350.00 up
 With Maggie Mixup face .... 400.00 up

L

Lady Churchill. 18" hp. (Margaret). 1953 .... 525.00
Lady Hamilton. 21" hp./vinyl arms (Cissy). 1957 . 500.00
 11" hp. (Cissette). 1957 .... 450.00
 21" (Jacqueline). 1968 .... 500.00
Lady in Waiting. 8" hp. (Wendy Ann). 1955 .... 650.00 up
Lady Lovelace. Cloth/felt. 1930's 300.00
Lady Windermere. 21" Compo. 1945 .... 500.00
Laughing Allerga. Cloth 300.00
Laurie Little Men. 8" hp. (Wendy Ann)
 1966-1972. Bend knees 125.00
 1973-1975. Straight legs. Marks: Alex 55.00
 Check pants 65.00
 1976 to date. Straight legs .... S.A.
 12" hp. (Lissy) 1967 .... 450.00
 12" Plastic/vinyl. (Nancy Drew) 1967 to date S.A.
Lazy Mary. 7" Compo. (Tiny Betty). 1936 ...... 165.00
Leslie. 17" Vinyl. (Black Polly). 1965-1971 ...... 225.00
 Bride. Discontinued 225.00
 In Formal. Discontinued 225.00
 In trunk/wardrobe .... 450.00 up
 Ballerina. Discontinued 185.00

Letty Bridesmaid. 7"-8" Compo. (Tiny Betty). 1938   165.00
Liesl: See Sound of Music.
Lila Bridesmaid. 7"-8" Compo. (Tiny Betty). 1938   165.00
Lil-Bet. Compo. (Prin. Eliz.) 350.00
Lissy. 11½"-12" hp. 1956-1958 .... 275.00
   8" 1961 Americana 425.00
   21" (Cissy)............................. 500.00
   21" (Coco) .... 1,500.00 up
   12" 1957 in windowbox/wardrobe .... 450.00 up
   Classics: See individual: McGuffey Ana,
Scarlett,
     Cinderella,
Little Angel. 9" Latex/vinyl 175.00
Little Audrey. Vinyl. 1954 .... 175.00
Little Betty. 9"-11" Compo. .... 175.00 up
Little Bitsey. 9" Cloth/vinyl. 1967 .... 85.00
Little Boy Blue. 7" Compo. (Tiny Betty). 1937 .. 165.00
Little Butch. 9" Cloth/vinyl. 1967 .... 85.00
Little Cherub. 11" Compo. 150.00
Little Colonel. 1935. 8½"-9" Compo. 175.00
   11"-13" Compo. 350.00- 450.00
   14"-17" 465.00- 565.00
   18"-23" 575.00- 650.00
   26"-27" 725.00
Little Dorrit. Cloth. 16" Dicken's Character 300.00
Little Emily. Cloth. 16" Dicken's Character 300.00
Little Genius. 1937. 12"-14" Compo./cloth 65.00
   18"-20" Compo./cloth 85.00
   8" hp./vinyl. 1957...................... 150.00
Little Godey. 8" hp. (Wendy Ann). 1953-1955 ... 425.00
Little Ice Queen. 8" hp. (Wendy Ann). 1958 ..... 225.00
Little Jack Horner. 7" Compo. (Tiny Betty). 1937   165.00
Little Granny. 14" Plastic/vinyl. (Mary Ann). 1966   200.00
Little Lady Doll. 8" hp. (Maggie Mixup). 1960 .. 325.00
   21" hp. 1949. Braids/Colonial dress 525.00
Little Lord Fauntlroy. Cloth 400.00
   13" Compo. (Wendy Ann). 1936 .... 325.00
Little Madaline (Madeline) 8" hp. 1953 .... 350.00
Little Melanie. 8" hp. (Wendy Ann). 1953-1957 .. 425.00
Little Men. 15" hp. (Margaret & Maggie). 1952 .. 500.00 each
Little Minister. 8" hp. (Wendy Ann). 1957 ...... 950.00 up
Little Nell. Cloth. 16" Dicken's Character 300.00
   14" Compo. (Wendy Ann). 1938 .... 275.00
Little Shaver. 10" Cloth. 1940 .... 225.00
   15" 325.00
   12" Plastic/vinyl. 1963 .... 200.00
Little Southern Boy/Girl. 10" Latex/vinyl. 1951 . 95.00
Little Southern Girl. 8" hp. (Wendy Ann). 1953 . 350.00
Little Victoria. 7½" 8". hp. (Wendy Ann). 1953-1954   425.00

Little Women. Cloth. (Meg, Jo, Amy, Beth). 1933.
16".. 300.00
7" Compo. (Tiny Betty). 1936-1939 .... 165.00
9" Compo. (Little Betty). 1937-1939 .... 200.00
13"-15" Compo. (Wendy Ann) 350.00
14"-15" hp. (Margaret & Maggie)
   1947-1956 (Plus Marme) .... 250.00 each
   1,325.00 set
14"-15" hp. (Margaret & Maggie)
   With bend knees (plus Marme)........... 275.00 each
   1,450.00 set
14"-15" Amy with loop curls 350.00
7½"-8" hp. (Wendy Ann). 1955. Also Marme. 150.00 each
   825.00 set
8" hp. (Wendy Ann). 1956-1959. Bend knees . 125.00 each
   700.00 set
8" Bend knees. 1960-1972................. 100.00 each
   575.00 set
8" Straight legs. Marks: Alex. 1973-1975.... 50.00 each
8" Straight legs. 1976 to date .... S.A.
11½"-12" hp. (Lissy). 1957-1966 .... 275.00 each
   1,450.00 set
12" Plastic/vinyl. (Nancy Drew)............ S.A.
Littlest Kitten. 8" vinyl. 1963 .... 125.00
Lively Huggums. 25". 1963................... 75.00
Lively Kitten. 14"-18". 1962 .... 75.00- 85.00
Lively Pussy Cat. 20" 75.00
Lola Bridesmaid. 7" Compo. (Tiny Betty). 1938.. 165.00
Lollie Bridesmaid. 7" Compo. (Tiny Betty). 1938. 165.00
Lollie Baby. 1941. Rubber/Compo............. 65.00
Looby Loo. 15½" hp. Ca. 1951-1954 .... 200.00
Louisa: See Sound of Music.
18" hp. (Margaret). 1952.................. 525.00
Lovey Dovey. 18"-19" Vinyl baby. 1958 .... 85.00
18"-19" hp./laytex. 1950 .... 75.00
Lucinda. 12" (Janie) Plastic/vinyl. 1969........ 250.00
14" (Mary Ann) Plastic/vinyl. 1971 .... S.A.
Lucy. 8" hp. (Wendy Ann) Americana. 1961..... 425.00
Lucy Bride. 14" hp. (Margaret)............... 225.00
17" hp. (Margaret) 225.00
16½" hp./vinyl arms. (Elise). 1958.......... 225.00
14" Compo. (Wendy Ann). 1939............ 200.00
17" Compo. (Wendy Ann) 250.00
21" Compo. (Wendy Ann) 275.00

M

Madame Doll. 21" hp./vinyl arms. (Coco). 1966 ..	1,500.00 up	
14" Plastic/vinyl. (Mary Ann) 1967-1974	250.00	
Madame Pompadour. 21" hp./vinyl arms.		
(Jacqueline). 1970	950.00	
Madelaine Du Bain. Compo. (Wendy Ann).		
1937-1939	325.00	
14" hp. (Maggie). 1949	325.00	
Madelaine. 14" Compo. (Wendy Ann). 1940	285.00	
17"-18" hp. 1952	300.00	
8" hp. 1954	350.00 up	
Madeline. 18" Rigid vinyl. 1961	250.00	
16½" (Kelly). 1964	250.00	
In trunk/wardrobe	450.00 up	
Madison, Dolly. President's Ladies. 1976	200.00	
Maggie. 15" hp. 1948	225.00	
17"-18"	250.00	
22"-23"	275.00	
17" Plastic/vinyl. (Elise) 1972-1973 only	250.00	
Maggie Mixup. 16½" hp./vinyl (Elise body). 1960	300.00	
17" Plastic/vinyl. 1961	275.00	
8" hp. 1960	275.00	
8" with Wendy Ann face. 1961	275.00	
8" hp. Angel. 1961	900.00 up	
8" in overalls/watering can	275.00	
8" in Skater outfit	275.00	
8" in riding habit	275.00	
Maggie Teenager. 15"-18" hp. 1951	225.00-	250.00
23"	275.00	
Maggie Walker. 15"-18" hp. 1949.	225.00-	250.00
20"-21"	250.00	
23"-25". 1952 (With Cissy face)	275.00-	300.00
Magnolia. 1977	350.00	
Maid of Honor. 18" Compo. (Wendy Ann)	250.00	
Majorette. 14"-17" Compo. (Wendy Ann)	400.00	
14" hp. (Margaret).1951	385.00	
8" hp. (Wendy Ann).....................	400.00	
Mama Kitten. 18"...........................	85.00	
Marcella Dolls. 13" to 24". Compo.		
Dressed in 1930's fashions. 1936	165.00-	225.00
March Hatter. Cloth/felt	300.00	
Margaret Rose: See Princess.		
Margaret O'Brien. 14½" Compo.	300.00	
17"-18"-19" Compo.	400.00-	550.00
21"-24" Compo.	650.00	
14½" Ballerina. Compo.	700.00	
14½" hp.	450.00	
17"-18" hp.	500.00	

21"-22" hp.	550.00	
Margot. 10"-11" hp. (Cissette). 1961	300.00	
Margot Ballerina. 15"-18" hp. (Margaret)	225.00-	400.00
1953-1954-1955 (Margaret & Maggie)	225.00	
15"-18" hp./vinyl arms. (Cissy). 1955	165.00-	185.00
Marionettes/Tony Sarg	165.00	
Marine. 14" Compo.	185.00	
Marketing. 8" hp. (Wendy Ann). 1955	145.00	
Marm Liza. 21" Compo. (Wendy Ann). 1938	500.00	
Maria. See Sound of Music.		
Marlo Thomas 17" Plastic/vinyl. (Polly). 1967	450.00	
Marme. See Little Women		
Marta. See Sound of Music		
Mary Ann. 14" Plastic/vinyl. 1965	250.00	
Mary-bel. (Doll That gets well)		
16" Rigid vinyl. 1959-1965	150.00	
In case	275.00	
In case with wardrobe	350.00	
In case/very long, straight hair	300.00	
Mary Cassatt Baby. 14" Cloth/vinyl. 1969	165.00	
20"	195.00	
Mary Ellen. 31" Rigid vinyl. 1954	300.00	
31" Plastic/vinyl. 1955	250.00	
Mary Ellen Playmate. 14" Plastic/vinyl. (Mary Ann)	385.00	
17" 1965 Exclusive	400.00	
Mary Louise. 21" Compo. (Wendy Ann). 1938	500.00	
18" hp. (Cissy). 1954	525.00	
8" hp. (Wendy Ann). 1954	425.00	
Mary Martin. 14"-17" hp. (Margaret). 1949	550.00	
In Sailor Suit	600.00	
Mary, Mary. 8" hp. (Wendy Ann). 1965-1972. Bend		
knees	100.00	
8" hp. Straight legs. 1973-1975. Marks: Alex	50.00	
8" hp. Straight legs. 1976 to date	S.A.	
Mary Mine. Cloth/vinyl. 14"-20" 1977	S.A.	
Mary Muslin. Pansy eyes. Cloth. 1951		
19"	300.00	
26"	350.00	
40"	400.00	
Mary Rose Bride. 17" hp. (Margaret). 1951	225.00	
Mary Sunshine. 15" Plastic/vinyl. 1961	225.00	
Matinee. 8" hp. (Wendy Ann). 1955	145.00	
May Pole Dance. 8" hp. (Wendy Ann). 1955	145.00	
7½" hp. 1953-1954	185.00	
McGuffey Ana. Cloth. 16"	300.00	
7" Compo. (Tiny Betty). 1935-1939	165.00	
9" Compo. (Little Betty). 1935-1939	200.00	
15" Compo. (Betty). 1935-1937	300.00	

13" Compo. (Wendy Ann). 1938	265.00
11"-13" Compo. (Prin. Eliz.). 1937	265.00
14"-16" Compo. (Prin. Eliz.).1937	300.00
17"-20" Compo. (Prin. Eliz.). 1937	345.00
21"-25" Compo. (Prin. Eliz.).1937	365.00
28" Compo. (Prin. Eliz.). 1937	425.00
17" Compo. (Margaret)	400.00
14½" hp. 1948	385.00
17"-18₀ hp.	400.00
21" hp. (Margaret)	450.00
12" hp. (Lissy). 1963	1,000.00 up
8" hp. (Wendy Ann). 1956	300.00
8" hp. (Wendy Ann). 1965	250.00
29" Cloth/vinyl. (Barbara Jane). 1952	300.00
14" Plastic/vinyl. (Mary Ann). 1968	175.00
14" Plastic/vinyl. (Mary Ann). 1978	S.A.
Meg. See Little Women.	
Melaine. 21" Compo. (Wendy Ann). 1945	500.00
Melanie. 21" hp./vinyl arms (Cissy). 1961 . . . . . . ,	475.00
21" (Coco). 1966	1,500.00 up
1967	550.00
1968	550.00
1969	425.00
1970	400.00
1971	400.00
1974	400.00
11" (Cissette). 1970	425.00
8" hp. (Wendy Ann). 1955-1956	425.00
Melinda. 11" hp. (Cissette). 1968	450.00
1969	450.00
14"-16" Plastic/vinyl. 1962-1963	225.00
14"Plastic/vinyl Ballerina. 1963	200.00
20" (Kelly). 1963	225.00
Mexico. 7" Compo. (Tiny Betty). 1936	125.00
9" Compo. (Little Betty). 1938	165.00
8" hp. (Wendy Ann). 1964-1972. Bend knees .	100.00
8" Straight legs. 1973-1975. Marks: Alex	50.00
8" Straight legs. 1976 to date	S.A.
Michael. 11" Plastic/vinyl. (Janie)	
1969. With Teddy Bear	300.00
Milly. 17" Plastic/vinyl. (Polly). 1968	225.00
Mimi. 30" Plastic/vinyl. 1961.	375.00
21" hp./vinyl arms. (Jacqueline). 1971	400.00
Miss America. (Holds flag). 14" Compo. 1940 . . .	200.00
Minister, Little. 8" hp. (Wendy Ann). 1955	950.00 up
Miss Muffett. 8" hp. (Wendy Ann). Bend knees.	
1965-1972	100.00
8" Straight legs. 1973-1975. Marks: Alex	50.00

8" Straight legs. 1976 to date . . . . S.A.
Miss U.S.A. 8" hp. (Wendy Ann)
   Discontinued. 1966-1968 . . . . 275.00
Miss Victory. 20" Compo. (Prin. Eliz.) 200.00
Mistress Mary. 7" Compo. (Tiny Betty). 1937 . . . 165.00
Molly Cottontail. Cloth/felt. 1930's 300.00
Mombo. 8" hp. (Wendy Ann). 1955 . . . . 165.00
Mommy & Me. 14" hp. (Margaret) 225.00
Monroe, Elizabeth. President's Ladies. 1976 . . . . 200.00
Morocco. 8" hp. (Wendy Ann)
   Discontinued. 1968-1970 . . . . 350.00
Mother and Me. 14"-15" and 9"
   Compo. (Wendy Ann & Little Betty). 1939-1942   275.00 set
Mrs. Buck Rabbit. Cloth/felt 300.00
Mrs. March Hare. Cloth/felt 300.00
Mrs. Quack-a-field. Cloth/felt 300.00
Mrs. Snoopie. Cloth/felt 300.00
Muffin. Cloth. 19". 1966 . . . . 75.00
   14" Discontinued. 1963 to 1978 . . . . 65.00

N

Nan McDare. Cloth/felt 300.00
Nana/Governess. 8" hp. (Wendy Ann). 1957 . . . . . 425.00 up
Nancy Ann. 17"-18". hp. 425.00
Nancy Drew. 12" Plastic/vinyl. 1967 . . . . 250.00
Nat. (Little Men). hp. 1952. (Maggie) 500.00
Netherland Boy & Girl: formerly Dutch.
   8" hp. 1974-1975. Straight legs. Marks: Alex   50.00
Nina Ballerina. 7" Compo. (Tiny Betty) 165.00
   14" hp. (Margaret). 1949 . . . . 225.00
   17" 300.00
   15" hp. (Margaret). 1951 . . . . 250.00
   19" 325.00
   23" 375.00
Normandy. 7" Compo. (Tiny Betty). 1935-1938 . . 125.00
Norway. 8" hp. (Wendy Ann). 1968-1972. Bend knees 100.00
   8" Straight legs. 1973-1975. Marks: Alex 50.00
   8" Straight legs. 1976 to date . . . . S.A.
Norwegian. 7"-8" Compo. (Tiny Betty). 1936 . . . . 125.00
   9" Compo. (Little Betty). 1938 . . . . 150.00
Nurse. 7" Compo. (Tiny Betty) 165.00
   13"-14" Compo. (Betty) 200.00
   14"-15" Compo. (Betty) 250.00
   15" Compo. (Prin. Eliz.) 250.00
   8" hp. (Wendy Ann). 1956 . . . . 450.00 up
   1961-1965 with baby . . . . 450.00 up

O

Old Fashioned Girl. 13" Compo. (Betty) 185.00
  20" hp. (Margaret). 1948 .... 185.00
  14" hp. (Margaret). 1948 .... 165.00
Oliver Twist. Cloth. 16" Dicken's Character. 1930's   400.00
  7" Compo. (Tiny Betty) 200.00
Oliver Twistail. Cloth/felt. 1930's 400.00
On Train. 8" hp. (Wendy Ann). 1955 .... 145.00
Orchard Princess. 21" Compo. (Wendy Ann) 500.00
Orphan Annie. 14" Plastic/vinyl. (Mary Ann). 1965   275.00

P

Pamela. 12" hp. (Lissy). Takes wigs. 1962 ...... 275.00
  In case 450.00
  12" Plastic/vinyl. (Nancy Drew) 375.00
  In case 425.00
Pan American-Pollera. 7" Compo. (Tiny Betty)
  1936 .... 165.00
Parlour Maid. 8" hp. (Wendy Ann). 1956 .... 900.00 up
Patchity Pam & Pepper. 15" Cloth. 1965 ...... 100.00
Patty. 18" Plastic/vinyl. (Melinda). 1965 .... 225.00
Patty Pigtails. 14" hp. 1949 .... 350.00
Peasant. 7" Compo. (Tiny Betty). 1936 .... 125.00
  9" Compo. (Little Betty). 1938-1939 .... 165.00
Peggy Bride. 14"-18" hp. (Margaret). 1950 ...... 225.00-   285.00
Penny. 34" Cloth/vinyl. 1951 .... 275.00
  42" 350.00
  7" Compo. (Tiny Betty). 1938 .... 165.00
Persia. 7" Compo. (Tiny Betty). 1936 .... 125.00
Peruvian Boy. 8" hp. (Wendy Ann)
  Discontinued. 1965-1966 .... 425.00
Peter Pan. 15" hp. (Margaret). 1953 .... 350.00
  8" hp. (Wendy Ann). 1953 .... 350.00
  14" Plastic/vinyl. (Mary Ann). 1969 .... 300.00
  Complete set of 4 dolls. 1969 .... 1,400.00
Picnic Day. 18" hp. (Margaret) 525.00
Pierrot Clown. 8" hp. (Wendy Ann). 1956 .... 950.00 up
Pinky. Cloth. 16" 300.00
  23" Baby. Compo. 1937 .... 85.00
  13"-19" Baby. Vinyl. 1954 .... 65.00-   85.00
  8" hp. (Wendy Ann). 1956 .... 275.00
  12" Plastic/vinyl. (Nancy Drew)
  1975 to date .... S.A.
Piper Laurie. 14" hp. (Margaret). 1950 .... 525.00
  21" 575.00
Pitty Pat. Cloth. 16" 300.00

Pitty Pat Clown	300.00	
Playing in the Garden.. 8" hp. (Wendy Ann). 1955	145.00	
Playmates. 29" Cloth. 1940	250.00	
Playing on the beach. 8" hp. (Wendy Ann). 1955.	145.00	
Pocahontas. 8" hp. (Wendy Ann)		
Discontinued. 1967-1970	350.00 up	
Poodles. Standing or sitting. 14"-17"	250.00-	350.00
Pollera (Pan American) 7" Compo. (Tiny Betty)		
1936	165.00	
Polish. 7" Compo. (Tiny Betty). 1935-1936	125.00	
8" hp. (Wendy Ann). Bend knees. 1964-1972 .	100.00	
8" Straight legs. 1973-1975. Marks: Alex....	50.00	
8" Straight legs. 1976 to date	S.A.	
Polly. 17" Plastic/vinyl. 1965 (Maria)...........	225.00	
In Ballgown	250.00	
In Street Dress	225.00	
Ballerina	185.00	
Bride	185.00	
In Trunk/Wardrobe. 1965	450.00 up	
Pollyana. 16" Rigid vinyl. 1960	200.00	
In formal...............................	250.00	
22"	250.00	
Polly Pigtails. 14½" hp. (Maggie)	225.00	
17"-17½"	275.00	
Polly Put Kettle On. 7" Compo. (Tiny Betty).1937	165.00	
Poor Cinderella. 14" hp. (Margaret). 1950	385.00	
14" Plastic/vinyl. (Mary Ann). 1967	S.A.	
Portrait Elise. 17" Plastic/vinyl. 1972		
Discontinued...............................	225.00	
Portugal. 8" hp. (Wendy Ann). Bend knees.		
1968-1972	100.00	
8" Straight legs. 1973-1975. Marks: Alex....	50.00	
8" Straight legs. 1976 to date	S.A.	
Precious. 12" Compo./cloth baby. 1937	85.00	
President's Ladies, 1st Set (Singles $200.00)	1,400.00 Set	
2nd Set (Singles $125.00)	750.00 Set	
Prince Charles. 8" hp. (Wendy Ann). 1957	275.00	
Prince Charming. 16"-17" Compo. (Margaret). 1947	425.00	
14"-15" hp. (Margaret)	495.00	
17"-18" hp. (Margaret). 1950	550.00	
21" hp. (Margaret)	600.00	
Prince Phillip. 17"-18" hp. (Margaret). 1953	450.00	
21"	550.00	
Princess Alexandria. 24" Cloth/compo. 1937	125.00	
Princess Doll. 13"-15"	125.00-	145.00
Princess Ann. 8" hp. (Wendy Ann). 1957	275.00	
Princess Elizabeth. 7" Compo. (Tiny Betty)	175.00	
8" With Dionne head.....................	175.00	

9"-11" Compo. (Little Betty)	175.00	
13" Compo. with closed mouth	275.00	
14". Compo.	250.00	
15" Compo.	275.00	
18"-19"	350.00	
24"	400.00	
28"	500.00	
Princess Flavia (Also Victoria) 21" Compo. (Wendy Ann). 1938-1945	500.00	
Princess Margaret Rose. 1937-1938		
15"-18" Compo. (Prin. Eliz.)	275.00	
21" Compo.	325.00	
14" hp. (Margaret). 1949-1953	250.00	
18" hp.	300.00	
Princess Rosetta. 17"-21" Compo. (Wendy Ann)	400.00-	500.00
Priscilla. 18" Cloth	300.00	
7" Compo. (Tiny Betty)	165.00	
8" hp. (Wendy Ann). 1965-1970. Discontinued	350.00	
Puddin'. 14"-21". Cloth/vinyl. Discontinued. 1976 (Name change)	75.00-	150.00
Pumkin'. 22" Cloth/vinyl. 1967 to date	85.00	
24" With rooted hair. 1976	95.00	
Pussy Cat. 14" Cloth/vinyl. 1965 to date	S.A.	
20"	S.A.	
24" Discontinued	95.00	
Black 14". Discontinued	110.00	
Black 20"	S.A	
In Trunk/trousseua. 14". 1966	450.00 up	

Q

Queen 18" hp. (Margaret). 1953	425.00	
8" hp. (Wendy Ann). 1954-1955	400.00	
10" hp. (Cissette). 1957	400.00	
1960	400.00	
1963	400.00	
21" hp./vinyl arms. (Sleeping Beauty). 1960	475.00	
20" hp./vinyl arms. (Cissy)		
1957-1958 White gown	525.00	
1961-1963 Gold gown	525.00	
Elise	300.00	
With Marybel head	300.00	
21" hp./vinyl arms. (Jacqueline) 1965	575.00	
1968	500.00	
11" hp. (Cissette). 1972-1973-1974	400.00	
In trunk/wardrobe. 1959	450.00 up	
Queen Alexandrine. 21" Compo. (Wendy Ann). 1939	450.00	

Quintuplets. hp. (Genius). 1964. (Fisher Quints) . .   425.00 set
Quiz-kins. 8" hp. (Wendy Ann). 1953 . . . .   300.00

R

Randolph, Martha. President's Ladies. 1976 . . . .   200.00
Rainy Day. 8" hp. (Wendy Ann). 1955 . . . .   145.00
Rebecca. 14"-17"-21" Compo. (Wendy Ann). 1940   275.00-   350.00
   14" hp. (Margaret) 325.00
   14" Plastic/vinyl. (Mary Ann)
     1968 Two tier skirt 200.00
     One piece skirt (1970 to date) . . . .   S.A.
Red Roy. 8" hp. (Wendy Ann). 1972. Bend knees   145.00
   1973-1975. Marks: Alex 100.00
   1976 to date . . . .   S.A.
Red Cross Nurse. 7" Compo. (Tiny Betty). 1937 .   165.00
   9" Compo. (Little Betty). 1939 . . . .   200.00
   14" hp. 350.00
Red Riding Hood. 7" Compo. (Tiny Betty). 1936 .   165.00
   9" Compo. (Little Betty). 1939 . . . .   200.00
   7½" hp. (Wendy Ann). 1955 . . . .   325.00
   8". 1956 . . . .   300.00
   8" hp. (Wendy Ann). Bend knees. 1962-1972 .   145.00
   8" Straight legs. 1973-1975. Marks: Alex 100.00
   8" Straight legs. 1976 to date . . . .   S.A.
Renoir. 21" Compo. (Wendy Ann). 1945 . . . .   500.00
   14" hp. (Margaret). 1950 . . . .   425.00
   21" hp./vinyl arms. (Cissy). 1961 . . . .   450.00
   18" hp./vinyl arms. (Elise). 1963 . . . .   450.00
   21" hp./vinyl arms. (Jacqueline). 1965 . . . .   450.00
     1966. (Coco) . . . .   1,500.00 up
     1967. . . . .   525.00
     1969 . . . .   525.00
     1970 . . . .   525.00
     1971 . . . .   450.00
     1972 . . . .   400.00
     1973 . . . .   400.00
     11" hp. (Cissette). 1968 . . . .   425.00
     1969 . . . .   425.00
     1970 . . . .   425.00
Renoir Child. 12" Plastic/vinyl. (Nancy Drew). 1967   275.00
   14". 1968. (Mary Ann) 275.00
Renoir Girl. 14" Plastic/vinyl. (Mary Ann).
1967-1968 . . . .   275.00
   1969-1971 . . . .   200.00
   1972 to date . . . .   S.A.
Renoir Mother. 21" hp./vinyl arms. (Jacqueline).
1967 . . . .   500.00
Riding Hood. Cloth/felt. 1930's 300.00
Riley's Little Annie. 14" Plastic/vinyl.
   (Mary Ann) 1967 . . . .   250.00

34

Ringbearer. hp. 14" (Lovey Dovey). 1951 . . . .   350.00
Rodeo. 8" hp. (Wendy Ann). 1955 . . . .   300.00
Roller Skating. 8 hp. (Wendy Ann). 1953-1955 . . .   185.00
Romance. 21" Compo. (Wendy Ann). 1945 . . . . . .   500.00
Romeo. 18" Compo. (Wendy Ann) 500.00
    8" hp. (Wendy Ann) 1955 . . . .   750.00 up
    12" Plastic/vinyl. (Nancy Drew). 1978 . . . .   S.A.
Rosamund Bridesmaid. 15" hp. (Margaret). 1951 .   265.00
    18" hp. 300.00
Rosebud. 16"-19" Cloth/vinyl. 1952-1953 . . . .   100.00
    23"-25" 125.00
Rose Fairy. 8" hp. (Wendy Ann) 500.00
Rosey Posey. 14" Cloth/vinyl. 1976 only. 125.00
Royal Evening. 18" hp. (Margaret). 1953 . . . .   525.00
Rozy. 12" Plastic/vinyl. (Janie). 1969 . . . .   200.00
Royal Wedding. 21" Compo. 500.00
Ruffles Clown. 21" 1954 . . . .   300.00
Rumbera-Rumbero. 7" Compo. (Tiny Betty) . . . . .   165.00 each
Rumania. 8" hp. (Wendy Ann). Bend knees.
    1968-1972 . . . .   100.00
    8" Straight legs. 1973-1975. Marks: Alex 50.00
    8" Straight legs. 1976 to date . . . .   S.A.
Russia. 8" hp. (Wendy Ann). Bend knees. 1968-1972   100.00
    8" Straight legs. 1973-1975. Marks: Alex 50.00
    8" Straight legs. 1976 to date . . . .   S.A.
Russian. 7" Compo. (Tiny Betty). 1935-1936 . . . .   165.00
Rusty. 20" Cloth/vinyl. 1967 . . . .   200.00

S

Sally Bride. 14" Compo. (Wendy Ann). 1938 . . . .   200.00
    18"-21" Compo. 225.00-   250.00
Sandy McHare. Cloth/felt. 1930's 300.00
Scarlett O'Hara. Pre-movie. 1936-1938
    7" Compo. (Tiny Betty) 200.00
    9" Compo. (Little Betty) 225.00
    10"-11"-13" (Wendy Ann) 300.00
    14"-16"-17" (Wendy Ann) 350.00-   450.00
    18"-21" Compo. (Wendy Ann) 450.00-   550.00
    21"-1945. Compo. (Wendy Ann) 550.00
    14"-16" hp. (Margaret) 425.00
    18" hp./vinyl arms (Elise) 1963 . . . .   325.00
    12" hp. (Lissy) 1963 . . . .   1,000.00 up
    21" (Cissy) 1955-1961 . . . .   500.00
    1962 . . . .   500.00
    7½"-8" hp. (Wendy Ann). 1955-1957 . . . .   325.00
    8" 1965 in white gown 300.00
    8" 1966-1972 (Flowered gown). Bend knees . .   350.00

8" 1973 to date (White gown)
Straight legs. Marks: Alex 50.00
Straight legs. 1976 to date . . . . S.A.
21" hp/vinyl arms. (Jacqueline). 1965 . . . . 525.00
1966 (Coco) . . . . 1,500.00 up
1967 . . . . 500.00
1968 . . . . 550.00
1969 . . . . 450.00
1970 . . . . 450.00
1975-1976 . . . . 375.00
1978 . . . . 350.00
11" hp. (Cissette). 1968-1973 . . . . 375.00
14" Plastic/vinyl. (Mary Ann). 1968 . . . . 350.00
School Girl. 7" Compo. (Tiny Betty) 165.00
8" hp. (Wendy Ann). 1955 . . . . 145.00
School Vistor's Day. 8" hp. (Wendy Ann). 1955 . 145.00
Scotch. 7" Compo. (Tiny Betty) 165.00
9" Compo. (Little Betty) 200.00
Scots Lass. 8" hp. (Wendy Ann). 1961-1963 . . . . . 275.00
With Maggie Mixup face. 1962 . . . . 325.00
Scottish. 8" hp. (Wendy Ann). Bend knees.
1964-1972 . . . . 100.00
8" Straight legs. 1973-1975. Marks: Alex 50.00
8" Straight legs. 1976 to date . . . . S.A.
Seven Dwarfs. Compo. 1937 . . . . 250.00 each
Shari Lewis. 14". 1959 . . . . 225.00
21" 350.00
Simone. 21" hp./vinyl arms. (Jacqueline).
1968. Trunk . . . . 650.00 up
Sir Lapin Hare. Cloth/felt. 1930's 300.00
Sir Winston Churchill. 18" hp. (Margaret). 1953 . 525.00
Sitting Pretty. 18" Foam body. 1965 . . . . 275.00
Skater's Waltz. 15"-18" (Cissy). 1955 . . . . 400.00
Skating Doll (Sonja Henie untagged) 185.00
Sleeping Beauty. 9" Compo. (Little Betty). 1941 . 200.00
15"-16" Compo. (Prin. Eliz.). 1938 . . . . 275.00
18"-21" (Wendy Ann) Compo. 350.00
10" hp. (Cissette). 1960 . . . . 375.00
16½" hp. 1959 . . . . 400.00
21". 1959 . . . . 475.00
14" Plastic/vinyl. (Mary Ann). 1971 to date . . S.A.
Slumbermate. 12" Cloth/compo 150.00
21" Compo/cloth 175.00
13" Vinyl/cloth. 1951 . . . . 85.00
Smarty. 12" Plastic/vinyl. 1962 . . . . 200.00
With boy "Artie" in case with wardrobe . . . . 550.00 up
Smiley. 20" Cloth/vinyl. 1971 . . . . 200.00
Smokey Tail. Cloth/felt. 1930's 300.00

Snow White. 13" Compo. Painted eyes. (Prin. Eliz.)

1937 .... 275.00
   12" Compo. (Prin. Eliz.) 200.00
   13" Compo. Sleep eyes. (Prin. Eliz.) 225.00
   16" Compo. (Prin. Eliz.) 275.00
   18" Compo. (Prin. Eliz.) 300.00
   15" hp. (Margaret). 1952 .... 350.00
   21" hp. (Margaret) 475.00
   14" Disney Crest Colors. (#1455) 1967 ...... 325.00
   8" hp. (Wendy Ann). Disney Crest Colors. 1972 300.00
   14" Plastic/vinyl. (Mary Ann). Disney Colors 325.00
   14" Plastic/vinyl. (Mary Ann). White gown.
     1968 to date .... S.A.
So Big. 22" Cloth/vinyl. 1968 to date .... S.A.
Soldier. 14" Compo. (Wendy Ann) 265.00
   17" Compo. (Wendy Ann) 300.00
Sonja Henie. 1939. 13"-15" Compo. 225.00
   7" Compo. (Tiny Betty).................... 225.00
   9" Compo. (Little Betty) 265.00
   11" Compo. (Wendy Ann) 200.00
   14" In case/wardrobe.................... 400.00
   17"-18" Compo. 395.00
   20"-22" Compo. 450.00
   13"-14" Compo. Jointed waist 275.00
   15"-18" hp./vinyl. 1951 .... 375.00- 475.00
   23" hp./vinyl........................... 325.00
Sound of Music. Large set. 14" Louisa 275.00
   11" Fredrich 225.00
   14" Brigitta, 14" Liesl.................... 225.00
   11" Marta, 11" Gretl..................... 165.00
   17" Maria 325.00
   Full set of 7 dolls. 1965-1970 .... 1,400.00
Sound of Music. Small set. 12" Maria 275.00
   8" Marta, 8" Fredrich, 8" Gretl 175.00
   11" Brigitta 175.00
   11" Liesl 250.00
   11" Louisa 300.00
   Set of 7 dolls, 1971-1973............... 1,200.00
Sound of Music. Dressed in sailor suits & tagged.
   Maria................................. 325.00
   Louisa 350.00
   Fredrich.............................. 275.00
   Brigitta 300.00
   Liesl................................. 300.00
   Gretl 250.00
   Marta 250.00
   Set 2,300.00
Southern Belle. 8" hp. (Wendy Ann). 1954-1956 . 325.00

8" hp. (Wendy Ann). 1963	325.00	
12" hp. (Lissy). 1963	1,000.00 up	
21" hp./vinyl arms. (Jacqueline). 1965	625.00	
1967	450.00	
11" hp. (Cissette). 1963-1973	400.00	
Southern Girl. 11"-14" Compo. (Wendy Ann)	265.00	
17"-21" Compo. (Wendy Ann)	300.00	
Spanish. 7"-8" Compo. (Tiny Betty). 1935-1939	125.00	
Spanish Boy. 8" hp. (Wendy Ann) Discontinued. 1964-1968	350.00 up	
Spanish Girl. 8" hp. (Wendy Ann). Bend knees. 1961-1972	100.00	
8" Straight legs. 1973-1975 Marks: Alex	50.00	
8" Straight legs. 1976 to date	S.A.	
Special Girl. 23"-24" Cloth/compo. 1942	285.00	
Story Princess. 15"-18" hp. (Margaret) (Cissy). 1954-1956	325.00	
8" hp. (Wendy Ann). 1956	300.00	
Stuffy (Boy) hp. (Margaret). 1952	500.00	
Suellen. 14"-17" Compo. (Wendy Ann). 1937	225.00-	300.00
Sugar Tears. 12" vinyl baby. 1964	95.00	
Sunbeam. 11"-16"-19". Newborn infant. 1951	95.00-	145.00
Sunbonnet Sue. 9" Compo. (Little Betty). 1937	200.00	
Sunday School. 8" hp. (Wendy Ann). 1955	145.00	
Sugar Darlin'. 14"-18". Cloth/vinyl. 1964	85.00	
24"	100.00	
Summer Morning. 8" hp. (Wendy Ann). 1955	145.00	
Sunflower. 40" Clown. Flower eyes. 1951	350.00	
Superior Quints. Compo. 8"	50.00 each	
	275.00 set	
Susie Q. Cloth. 1940	500.00 up	
Suzy. 12" Plastic/vinyl. (Janie). 1970	200.00	
Sweden. 8" hp. (Wendy Ann). Bend knees. 1961-1972	100.00	
With Maggie Mixup Face	150.00	
8" Straight legs. 1973-1975. Marks: Alex	50.00	
8" Straight legs. 1976 to date	S.A.	
Swedish. 7" Compo. (Tiny Betty)	125.00	
Sweet Baby. Cloth/laytex. 18½"-20". 1948	65.00	
Sweet Tears. 9" vinyl. 1965-1974	85.00	
With layette in box	165.00	
13"-14" in trunk/trousseau	350.00 up	
14" 1965 to date	S.A.	
16" 1965-1972	85.00	
Sweet Violet. 18" hp. (Cissy). 1951-1954	325.00	
Sweetie Baby. 22". 1962	100.00	
Sweetie Walker. 23". 1962	150.00	
Swimming. 8" hp. (Wendy Ann). 1955	145.00	
Swiss. 7" (Compo). (Tiny Betty). 1936	165.00	

```
8" hp. (Wendy Ann). Bend knees. 1961-1972 .    100.00
8" Straight legs. 1973-1975. Marks: Alex....     50.00
8" Straight legs. 1976 to date ............     S.A.
```

T

```
Tea Party. 8" hp. (Wendy Ann). 1955 ..........    145.00
Tennis. 8" hp. (Wendy Ann) .................      145.00
Thailand. 8" hp. (Wendy Ann). Bend knees.
  1966-1972 ..............................        100.00
    8" Straight legs. 1973-1975. Marks: Alex....   50.00
    8" Straight legs. 1976 to date ............    S.A.
The Enchanted Doll. Enchanted Doll House Special
  8" (Wendy Ann). 1980-$325.00. 1981 .........    275.00
Three Pigs & Wolf. Compo. 1938 .............     250.00 each
Timmy Toddler. 23" Plastic/vinyl. 1960 ........   95.00-  125.00
    30" ..................................        165.00
Tinkerbelle. 11" hp. (Cissette). 1969 ...........  300.00
    8" hp. (Wendy Ann).....................        225.00
Tiny Betty. 7"-8" Compo. ..................        150.00
Tiny Tim. Compo. (Wendy Ann). 14"-1938 ......     185.00
Tippy Toe. Cloth. 16" ....................        300.00
Tommy. 12" hp. (Lissy). 1962 ............... 1,000.00 up
Tommy Bangs. hp. (Maggie). 1952 .............     425.00
Tony Sarg: Marionettes.....................       165.00
Topsy-Turvy. Compo. with Tiny Betty heads. 1935  150.00
    With Dionne Quint heads. 1936............      175.00
Turkey. 8" hp. (Wendy Ann). Bend knees. 1968-1972 100.00
    8" Straight legs. 1973-1975. Marks: Alex....   50.00
    8" Straight legs. 1976 to date ............    S.A.
Tweedle-Dum & Tweedle-Dee. Cloth. 14" .......     300.00 each
Tyrolean Boy. 1962-1973. Became Austria 1974 .    135.00
Tyrolean Girl. 1962-1973. Became Austria 1974 .   125.00
```

U

```
United States. 8" hp. (Wendy Ann)
    1974-1975. Straight legs. Marks: Alex ......   125.00
    1976 to date. Straight legs ...............    S.A.
    Tag reading "Untied States"..............      200.00
```

V

```
Victoria. 21" Compo. (Wendy Ann). 1938 .......    500.00
    21" Compo. (Flavia). 1945.................     500.00
    14" hp. (Margaret). 1950 .................     325.00
    18" hp. (Margaret). 1954 .................     350.00
```

8" hp. (Wendy Ann). 1953-1954	400.00	
18" Baby. 1966	85.00	
20" Baby. 1967 to date	S.A.	
Victorian. 18" hp. (Margaret). 1953	425.00	
Vietnam. 8" hp. (Wendy Ann)		
Discontinued. 1968-1969	400.00	
With Maggie Mixup face	475.00	
Violet. See Sweet Violet.		
Virginia Dare. 9" Compo. (Little Betty). 1940	175.00	

W

W.A.A.C. 14" Compo. (Wendy Ann)	185.00	
W.A.A.F. 14" Compo. (Wendy Ann)	185.00	
W.A.V.E. 14" Compo. (Wendy Ann)	185.00	
Walking Her Dog. 8" hp. (Wendy Ann). 1955	150.00	
Waltzing. 8" hp. (Wendy Ann). 1955	250.00	
Washington, Martha. President's Ladies. 1976	300.00	
Wendy (Peter Pan) 15" hp. (Margaret). 1953	275.00	
14" Plastic/vinyl. (Mary Ann). 1969	250.00	
Wendy Angel. 8" hp. (Wendy Ann). 1954	900.00 up	
Wendy Ann. 11"-15" Compo.	325.00	
In riding habit	200.00	
17"-21" Compo.	350.00-	450.00
14½"-17" hp. 1948.	225.00-	250.00
16"-22" hp	250.00-	325.00
23"-25" hp. 1949	400.00	
7½" hp.	145.00	
8" hp. Bend knees	125.00	
Wendy Bride. 14"-22" Compo. (Wendy Ann)	200.00-	250.00
15"-18" hp. (Margaret). 1951	225.00-	265.00
23" hp. (Margaret). 1951	350.00	
8" hp. (Wendy Ann). 1955	200.00	
Wendy Bridesmaid. 8" hp. (Wendy Ann). 1955	175.00	
White Rabbit. Cloth/felt	300.00	
Winnie Walker. 15" hp. (Cissy). 1953	165.00	
18"-23"	200.00-	250.00
In trunk/trousseau	650.00 up	

Y

Yolanda. 12" (Brenda Starr). 1965	165.00	
Yugoslavia. 8" hp. (Wendy Ann). Bend knees.		
1968-1972	100.00	
8" Straight legs. 1973-1975. Marks: Alex	50.00	
8" Straight legs. 1976 to date	S.A.	

Z

Zorina Ballerina. 17" Compo.		
(Wendy Ann). 1937	325.00	